ELEMENTARY

Over 170 reproducible tools to help with classroom management!

- Monthly calendars
- Special schedules
- Planning calendars
- Substitute teacher forms
- Curriculum helpers
- Assessment forms
- Parent communication forms

- Open house helpers
- Parent-teacher conference forms
- Seasonal newsletters
- Awards
- Teacher notes
- ...and lots more!

Editorial Team: Becky S. Andrews, Debbie Ashworth, Diane Badden, Kimberley Bruck, Karen A. Brudnak, Pam Crane, Chris Curry, Pierce Foster, Tazmen Hansen, Marsha Heim, Lori Z. Henry, Debra Liverman, Kitty Lowrance, Gerri Primak, Mark Rainey, Greg D. Rieves, Hope Rodgers-Medina, Rebecca Saunders, Donna K. Teal, Sharon M. Tresino, Zane Williard

FREE Online Extras!

Follow these steps to get your **FREE** online extras!
1. Go to www.themailbox.com.
2. Click on "Register."
3. Register your copy of *The Ultimate Forms for All Reasons.* Your item number is 61337.

www.themailbox.com

©2012 The Mailbox® Books
All rights reserved.
ISBN #978-1-61276-152-7

Printed in the United States
10 9 8 7 6 5 4 3 2 1

HPS 233453

Table of Contents

Classroom Management

Contact Log

Contact Log

Student: _____

Parent: _____

Date: _____

Reason for co___

Me___

☐ ph___

☐ em___

Homework Assignment Sheet

Homework for the Week

of _____

_____
parent signature

Special Class Schedule

_____
teacher

_____
grade

Special Class S___

Class		Monday	Tuesday	Wednesday	Thu___
MUSIC Time:					
PE Time:					
MEDIA CENTER Time:					
ART Time:					
COMPUTER Time:					

Transportation

Transportation After School

Room # _____ Grade _____

Teacher _____

Car Riders

Bus Riders

August

Sunday	Monday	Tuesday	Wednesday	Thursday	Friday	Saturday

The Ultimate Forms for All Reasons • ©The Mailbox® Books • TEC61337

September

Sunday	Monday	Tuesday	Wednesday	Thursday	Friday	Saturday

October

Sunday	Monday	Tuesday	Wednesday	Thursday	Friday	Saturday

November

Sunday	Monday	Tuesday	Wednesday	Thursday	Friday	Saturday

The Ultimate Forms for All Reasons • ©The Mailbox® Books • TEC61337

December

Sunday	Monday	Tuesday	Wednesday	Thursday	Friday	Saturday

The Ultimate Forms for All Reasons • ©The Mailbox® Books • TEC61337

January

Sunday	Monday	Tuesday	Wednesday	Thursday	Friday	Saturday

February

Sunday	Monday	Tuesday	Wednesday	Thursday	Friday	Saturday

The Ultimate Forms for All Reasons • ©The Mailbox® Books • TEC61337

March

Calendar

Sunday	Monday	Tuesday	Wednesday	Thursday	Friday	Saturday

The Ultimate Forms for All Reasons • ©The Mailbox® Books • TEC61337

11

April

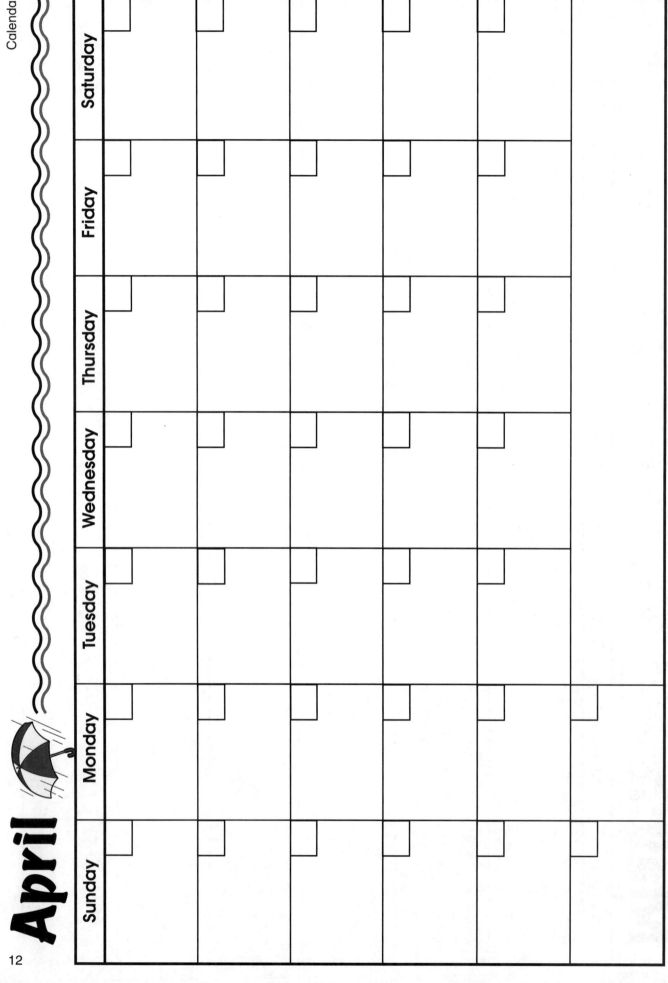

Sunday	Monday	Tuesday	Wednesday	Thursday	Friday	Saturday

The Ultimate Forms for All Reasons • ©The Mailbox® Books • TEC61337

May

Sunday	Monday	Tuesday	Wednesday	Thursday	Friday	Saturday

June

Sunday	Monday	Tuesday	Wednesday	Thursday	Friday	Saturday

The Ultimate Forms for All Reasons • ©The Mailbox® Books • TEC61337

July

Sunday	Monday	Tuesday	Wednesday	Thursday	Friday	Saturday

The Ultimate Forms for All Reasons • ©The Mailbox® Books • TEC61337

Student Information Card

student number

first name _____ last name _____

address _____

city _____ state _____ zip _____ home phone _____

mother's name _____ mother's work phone _____ mother's cell phone _____

father's name _____ father's work phone _____ father's cell phone _____

primary email _____ student's birthdate _____

Comments: _____

_____

_____ emergency contact _____

_____ emergency phone _____

The Ultimate Forms for All Reasons • ©The Mailbox® Books • TEC61337

Student Information Card

student number

first name _____ last name _____

address _____

city _____ state _____ zip _____ home phone _____

mother's name _____ mother's work phone _____ mother's cell phone _____

father's name _____ father's work phone _____ father's cell phone _____

primary email _____ student's birthdate _____

Comments: _____

_____

_____ emergency contact _____

_____ emergency phone _____

The Ultimate Forms for All Reasons • ©The Mailbox® Books • TEC61337

Class Information

Student Name	Birthday	Parent(s) Name(s)	Phone number(s)
1.			
2.			
3.			
4.			
5.			
6.			
7.			
8.			
9.			
10.			
11.			
12.			
13.			
14.			
15.			
16.			
17.			
18.			
19.			
20.			
21.			
22.			
23.			
24.			
25.			
26.			
27.			
28.			
29.			
30.			

Transportation After School

Teacher _____ Room # _____ Grade _____

Car Riders

_____   _____   _____

_____   _____   _____

_____   _____   _____

_____   _____   _____

Bus Riders

Walkers

_____   _____

_____   _____

_____   _____

_____   _____

_____   _____

Other

_____

_____

_____

_____

_____

The Ultimate Forms for All Reasons • ©The Mailbox® Books • TEC61337

1.															
2.															
3.															
4.															
5.															
6.															
7.															
8.															
9.															
10.															
11.															
12.															
13.															
14.															
15.															
16.															
17.															
18.															
19.															
20.															
21.															
22.															
23.															
24.															
25.															
26.															
27.															
28.															
29.															
30.															

teacher

grade

Weekly Schedule

Time	Activity	M	T	W	Th	F
—						
—						
—						
—						
—						
—						
—						
—						
—						
—						
—						
—						
—						

Special instructions:

Special Class Schedule

teacher _____   grade _____

Class	Monday	Tuesday	Wednesday	Thursday	Friday
MUSIC Time:					
PE Time:					
MEDIA CENTER Time:					
ART Time:					
COMPUTER Time:					
Time:					

Students attending other classes (speech, band, etc.): _____

_____

Students Who Visit a Specialist

Student	Day(s)	Time	Specialist, room number, phone extension

Additional notes:

Our Class Rules

Behavior

_____
_____
_____
_____
_____

School and Classroom

_____
_____
_____
_____
_____

Homework

_____
_____
_____

Rewards

We have discussed the rules we need in our classroom in order to have a positive learning environment. I agree to do my part and follow these rules.

Signed, _____ this _____ day of _____.

Homework Policy

Dear Parent,

Homework is an important part of your child's school experience. Supporting good work habits requires a joint effort. I will support your child and encourage good work habits at school. Your child will benefit greatly from your support and encouragement at home.

Please read the homework policy below and discuss it with your child. **Then sign the lower portion of this form and return it to school with your child.** Be sure to keep this portion of the form for future reference.

_____

_____

_____

_____

_____

_____

Rewards: _____

_____

_____

Sincerely,

_____
teacher

_____
date

The Ultimate Forms for All Reasons • ©The Mailbox® Books • TEC61337

I have read the homework policy.
I have also discussed the policy with my child.

_____   _____
parent signature   student name

_____
date

Homework for the Week

of _____

Monday

_____
parent signature

Tuesday

_____
parent signature

Wednesday

_____
parent signature

Thursday

_____
parent signature

Friday

_____
parent signature

Homework Excuse

Dear _____ ,

teacher

I did not do the following homework assignment(s):

I did not do the assignment(s) because

Here is how I plan to make up the assignment(s):

Sincerely,

_____   _____
parent signature   student signature

Behavior and Discipline Policies

Dear Parent,

   Your child's success is very important. To create and maintain a positive learning environment for all students, I will follow the behavior and discipline policies below. Please read them and discuss them with your child. **Then sign the lower portion of this form and return it to school with your child.** Be sure to keep this portion of the form for future reference.

Behavior Policy

_____

_____

_____

Rewards for good behavior: _____

_____

Discipline Policy

_____

_____

_____

Sincerely,

_____
teacher

_____
date

The Ultimate Forms for All Reasons • ©The Mailbox® Books • TEC61337

- -

I have read the behavior and discipline policies. I have also discussed these policies with my child.

_____   _____
parent signature   student name

_____
date

Behavior Documentation

Teacher: _____   Grade: ___   Room No.: ___

Student Name	Date	Behavior	Action Taken	Parent Contact/Response

Behavior Log for _____
student

Date: _____ Time of incident: _____ Location: _____

⬤ **The rule that I did not follow is** _____

_____

_____

_____

⬤ **I did not make a good choice when I** _____

_____

_____

_____

⬤ **I made that choice because** _____

_____

_____

_____

⬤ **I should have** _____

_____

_____

_____

_____   _____
student signature   **teacher signature**

Teacher's comments:

Contact Log

Student: _____

Parent: _____

Date: _____ Time: _____ Method of contact: ☐ phone ☐ in person ☐ email ☐ _____	Reason for contact:	Notes:
Date: _____ Time: _____ Method of contact: ☐ phone ☐ in person ☐ email ☐ _____	Reason for contact:	Notes:
Date: _____ Time: _____ Method of contact: ☐ phone ☐ in person ☐ email ☐ _____	Reason for contact:	Notes:
Date: _____ Time: _____ Method of contact: ☐ phone ☐ in person ☐ email ☐ _____	Reason for contact:	Notes:

The Ultimate Forms for All Reasons •©The Mailbox® Books • TEC61337

Today's Meeting ••••••••••••••••••••••••••••

Type of Meeting: Staff   Grade Level   IEP   Other: _____

Date: _____   Time: _____

Purpose of meeting: _____

Attendees: _____

Notes:

Important points and/or dates:

_____ 's Lending Log
teacher name

Sharing between teachers is great!
Please sign your name, item, and the date.

Date Borrowed	Name of Borrower	Item Borrowed	Date Returned

The Ultimate Forms for All Reasons • ©The Mailbox® Books • TEC61337

My Shopping List

_____
teacher

Date items needed: _____

Store(s): _____

_____

☐ _____

☐ _____

☐ _____

☐ _____

☐ _____

☐ _____

☐ _____

☐ _____

☐ _____

☐ _____

☐ _____

☐ _____

Be sure to save your
receipts for tax purposes.

The Ultimate Forms for All Reasons • ©The Mailbox® Books • TEC61337

My Shopping List

_____
teacher

Date items needed: _____

Store(s): _____

_____

☐ _____

☐ _____

☐ _____

☐ _____

☐ _____

☐ _____

☐ _____

☐ _____

☐ _____

☐ _____

☐ _____

☐ _____

Be sure to save your
receipts for tax purposes.

The Ultimate Forms for All Reasons • ©The Mailbox® Books • TEC61337

Daily To-Do List

Date _____

(✓ = completed   • = do tomorrow)

To do **BEFORE** school:

☐ ☐ ☐

☐ ☐ ☐

To do **DURING** school:

☐ ☐ ☐

☐ ☐ ☐

To do **AFTER** school:

☐ ☐ ☐ ☐

☐ ☐ ☐ ☐

The Ultimate Forms for All Reasons • ©The Mailbox® Books • TEC61337

Daily To-Do List

Date _____

(✓ = completed   • = do tomorrow)

To do **BEFORE** school:

☐ ☐ ☐

☐ ☐ ☐

To do **DURING** school:

☐ ☐ ☐

☐ ☐ ☐

To do **AFTER** school:

☐ ☐ ☐ ☐

☐ ☐ ☐ ☐

The Ultimate Forms for All Reasons • ©The Mailbox® Books • TEC61337

Rounding Up Volunteers!

Dear Parent,

It is helpful for me to gather information about my students' parents and other potential volunteers for upcoming projects, events, and general classroom help. I encourage you to share your interests and talents with our class. Please complete the form below and return it to school. I will contact you for volunteer opportunities.

Sincerely,

_____
teacher signature

- -

Your name: _____ Student: _____

My special interests or hobbies: _____

_____

My profession: _____

I would like to contribute by

☐ helping in the classroom   ☐ supplying materials   ☐ going on field trips

☐ making projects at home   ☐ making phone calls   ☐ supplying snacks

☐ _____

If you would like to help in the classroom, please list the day(s) and time(s) that work

best for you. _____

_____

Additional information:

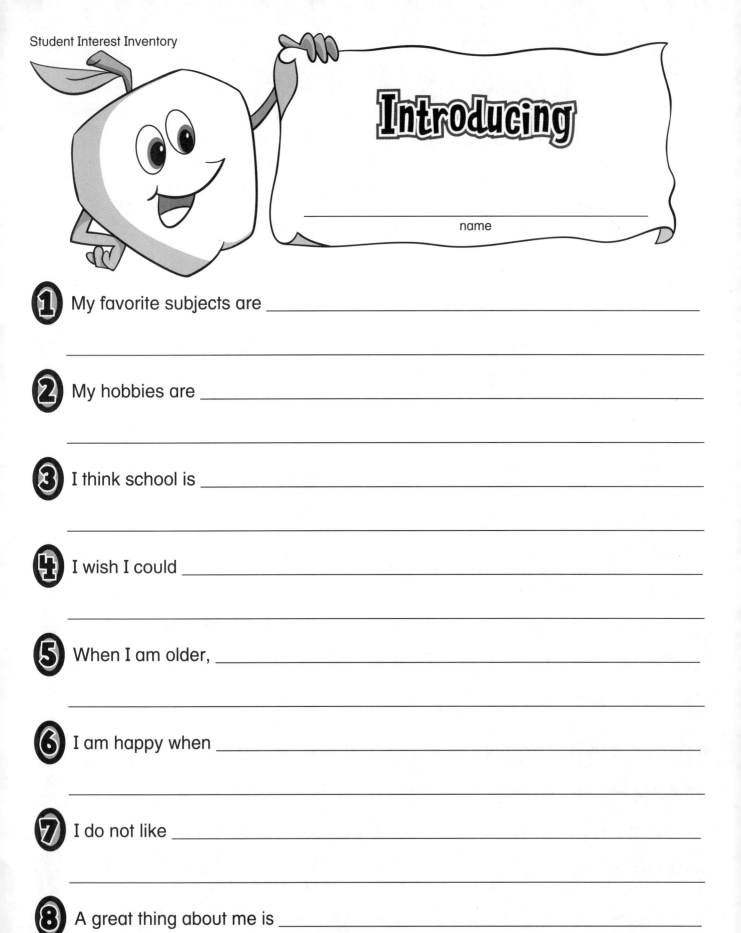

Introducing

_____
name

1 My favorite subjects are _____

_____

2 My hobbies are _____

_____

3 I think school is _____

_____

4 I wish I could _____

_____

5 When I am older, _____

_____

6 I am happy when _____

_____

7 I do not like _____

_____

8 A great thing about me is _____

_____

Hall Pass

_____
teacher

Restroom Pass

_____
teacher

Computer Lab Pass

_____
teacher

MEDIA CENTER PASS

_____
teacher

Desk Labels

Aa Bb Cc Dd Ee Ff Gg Hh Ii Jj Kk Ll Mm

Nn Oo Pp Qq Rr Ss Tt Uu Vv Ww Xx Yy Zz

The Ultimate Forms for All Reasons • ©The Mailbox® Books • TEC61337

Aa Bb Cc Dd Ee Ff Gg Hh Ii Jj Kk Ll Mm

Nn Oo Pp Qq Rr Ss Tt Uu Vv Ww Xx Yy Zz

The Ultimate Forms for All Reasons • ©The Mailbox® Books • TEC61337

The Ultimate Forms for All Reasons • ©The Mailbox® Books • TEC61337

The Ultimate Forms for All Reasons • ©The Mailbox® Books • TEC61337

Good Work Coupon
Redeem this coupon for

_____

_____

_____

student

TEC61337

Good Work Coupon
Redeem this coupon for

_____

_____

_____

student

TEC61337

Good Work Coupon
Redeem this coupon for

_____

_____

_____

student

TEC61337

Good Work Coupon
Redeem this coupon for

_____

_____

_____

student

TEC61337

Good Behavior Coupon
Redeem this coupon for

_____

_____

_____

student

TEC61337

Good Behavior Coupon
Redeem this coupon for

_____

_____

_____

student

TEC61337

Good Behavior Coupon
Redeem this coupon for

_____

_____

_____

student

WAY TO GO!

TEC61337

Good Behavior Coupon
Redeem this coupon for

_____

_____

_____

student

TEC61337

Name _____ Dates _____

Name _____ Dates _____

Name _____ Dates _____

The Ultimate Forms for All Reasons • ©The Mailbox® Books • TEC61337

Name _____ Dates _____

The Ultimate Forms for All Reasons • ©The Mailbox® Books • TEC61337

Name _____   Dates _____

The Ultimate Forms for All Reasons • ©The Mailbox® Books • TEC61337

Name _____   Dates _____

The Ultimate Forms for All Reasons • ©The Mailbox® Books • TEC61337

Name _____ Dates _____

The Ultimate Forms for All Reasons • ©The Mailbox® Books • TEC61337

Name _____ Dates _____

The Ultimate Forms for All Reasons • ©The Mailbox® Books • TEC61337

Name _____ Dates _____

The Ultimate Forms for All Reasons • ©The Mailbox® Books • TEC61337

Name _____ Dates _____

The Ultimate Forms for All Reasons • ©The Mailbox® Books • TEC61337

Name _____ Dates _____

Name _____ Dates _____

Star of the Week

_____
name

_____
week

Birthdate: _____ Age: _____

Siblings: _____

_____

My Favorites

Food: _____ Color: _____

Sport: _____ Subject: _____

Book: _____

Game: _____

When I grow up, I want to be _____

_____

I'm special because _____

_____

_____

Note to the teacher: Have the student star of the week complete this page at home and return it to school with some photos or illustrations to correspond with his responses.

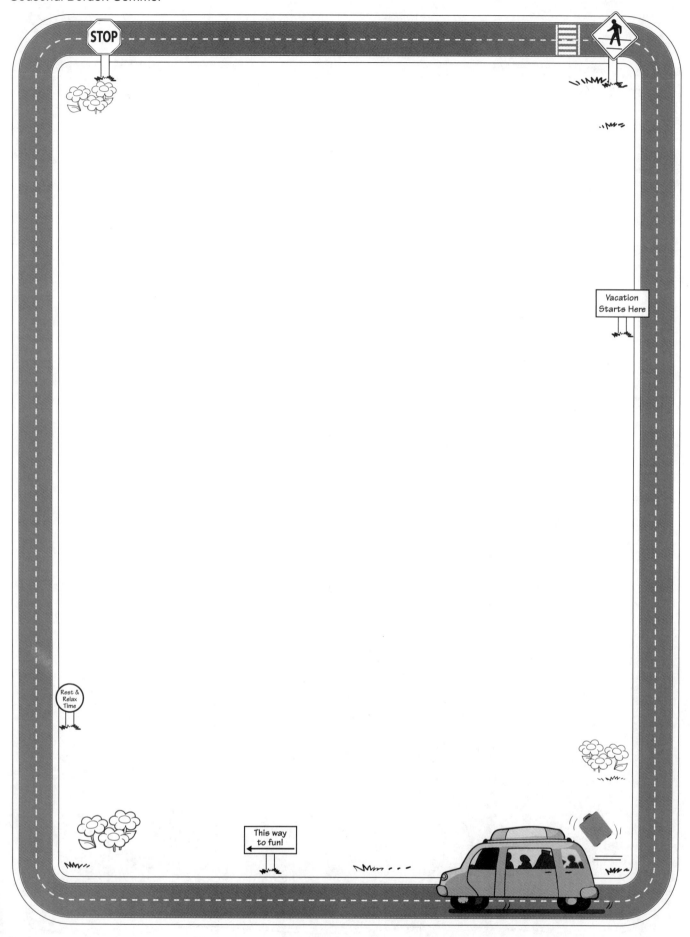

STOP

Vacation
Starts Here

Rest &
Relax
Time

This way
to fun!

Planning & Instruction

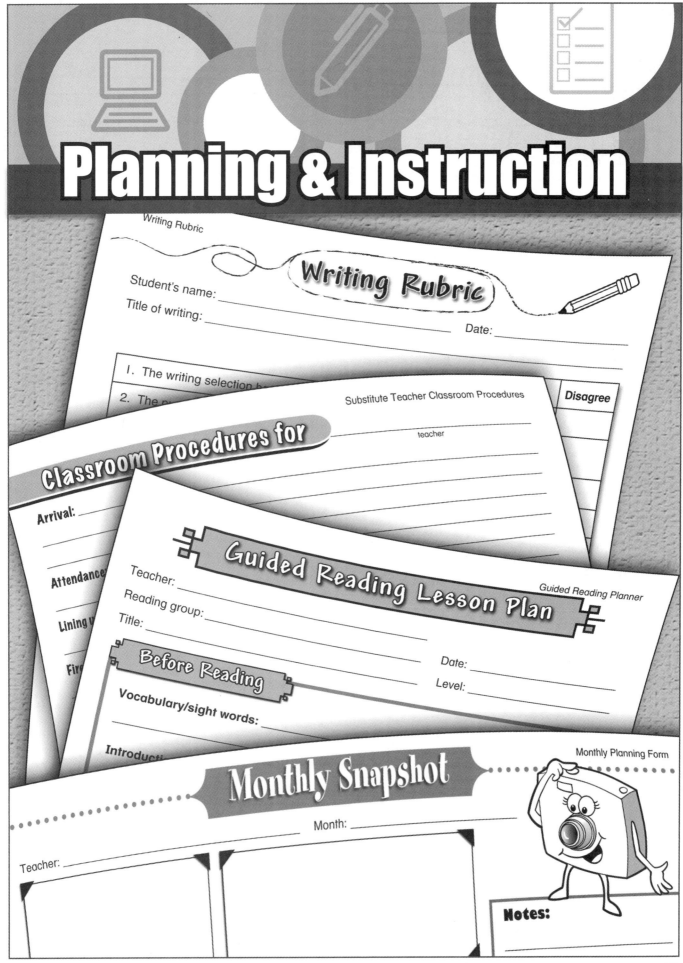

Writing Rubric

Writing Rubric

Student's name: _____

Title of writing: _____

Date: _____

1. The writing selection _____
2. The _____

Substitute Teacher Classroom Procedures

teacher _____

Disagree

Classroom Procedures for

Arrival: _____

Attendance _____

Lining u _____

Fir _____

Guided Reading Planner

Guided Reading Lesson Plan

Teacher: _____

Reading group: _____

Title: _____

Date: _____

Level: _____

Before Reading

Vocabulary/sight words: _____

Introduct

Monthly Planning Form

Monthly Snapshot

Month: _____

Teacher: _____

Notes:

Yearly Planning Calendar

August

September

October

November

Yearly Planning Calendar

_____

teacher

_____

grade

December

January

February ♡

March

Yearly Planning Calendar

_____
teacher

_____
grade

 April

 May

 June

 July

Monthly Snapshot

Teacher: _____

Month: _____

Notes:

The Ultimate Forms for All Reasons • ©The Mailbox® Books • TEC61337

Note to the teacher: At the beginning of each month, make a copy of this page. Program each section with information such as to-do lists, birthdays, special events, meetings, duties, and materials to collect. Then use the sheet to plan for the month.

Weekly Plan

Week of

Monday

Tuesday

Wednesday

Thursday

Friday

Notes

Meeting Notes

_____ _____
date   time

Attendees
_____

_____

_____

Notes

Next Steps

Comments: _____

_____

Reading Group _____

Student	Reading Level

Reading Group _____

Student	Reading Level

Reading Group _____

Student	Reading Level

Reading Group _____

Student	Reading Level

Reading Group _____

Student	Reading Level

Reading Group _____

Student	Reading Level

Guided Reading Lesson Plan

Teacher: _____

Reading group: _____   Date: _____

Title: _____   Level: _____

Before Reading

Vocabulary/sight words: _____

_____

Introduction: _____

_____

Comprehension strategies:

☐ making inferences   ☐ cause and effect   ☐ fact and opinion

☐ visualizing   ☐ summarizing   ☐ sequencing

☐ compare and contrast   ☐ author's purpose   ☐ making connections

☐ drawing conclusions   ☐ main idea and details   ☐ other _____

During Reading

☐ shared reading   ☐ partner reading   ☐ independent reading

Teaching points: _____

_____

_____

After Reading

Revisit vocabulary, comprehension strategies, and teaching points.

Story discussion points: _____

_____

_____

Writing follow-up: _____

_____

School Information

General Information

Teacher _____ Grade level _____

Room # _____ Phone extension _____

Principal _____

Assistant Principal _____

Secretary _____

Nurse _____

Guidance Counselor _____

Custodian _____

Aide(s) _____

Grade-Level Teachers

Name _____ Room # _____ Ext. _____

Name _____ Room # _____ Ext. _____

Name _____ Room # _____ Ext. _____

Name _____ Room # _____ Ext. _____

Special Teachers

	Name	Day	Time	Location	Ext.
Music					
Art					
PE					
Media					
Other					

Children With Special Needs (name and special need)

_____

_____

_____

_____

Classroom Procedures for

_____
teacher

Arrival: _____

_____

_____

Attendance: _____

_____

Lining up: _____

_____

Fire drill: _____

_____

Recess: _____

_____

Lunch/milk count: _____

_____

Restroom break: _____

_____

Behavior policy/discipline: _____

_____

Free time: _____

_____

Dismissal: _____

_____

Student Pull-Outs for Special Programs

Name	Class	Day/Time

Helpful students: _____

_____

Substitute Teacher Class Information

Classroom Information for

teacher

Student Name	Transportation Info	Daytime Phone No.	Parent(s) Name(s)
1.			
2.			
3.			
4.			
5.			
6.			
7.			
8.			
9.			
10.			
11.			
12.			
13.			
14.			
15.			
16.			
17.			
18.			
19.			
20.			
21.			
22.			
23.			
24.			
25.			
26.			
27.			
28.			
29.			
30.			

The Ultimate Forms for All Reasons • ©The Mailbox® Books • TEC61337

 **Emergency Lesson Plan for** _____ _____ _____
teacher   grade   room number

Subject:

Subject:

Subject:

Subject:

Subject:

A Note From the Sub

_____   _____
teacher   date

Today we were able to accomplish _____

_____

_____

_____

Problems I encountered were _____

_____

_____

_____

What I found most helpful was _____

_____

_____

_____

Additional comments _____

_____

_____

_____

_____

_____

The Ultimate Forms for All Reasons • ©The Mailbox® Books • TEC61337

_____'s

Journal

COOL

AWESOME

_____'s

Journal

_____'s

Journal

'S

Journal

Reading Contract

_____
date

I, _____, agree to read _____.
        student   number of books or pages

To do this, I will need to read _____
                                   pages or minutes

each day. I plan to complete this contract by

_____. I will keep
        date

a record of my progress.

_____
student signature

_____
teacher signature

The Ultimate Forms for All Reasons • ©The Mailbox® Books • TEC61337

Reading Contract

_____
date

I, _____, agree to read _____.
        student   number of books or pages

To do this, I will need to read _____
                                   pages or minutes

each day. I plan to complete this contract by

_____. I will keep
        date

a record of my progress.

_____
student signature

_____
teacher signature

The Ultimate Forms for All Reasons • ©The Mailbox® Books • TEC61337

Name _____

Home Reading Record

Date	Title (or Type of Material Read)	Minutes	Pages	Parent Initials

Sequencing Chart

Name _____

Date _____

Book title and author: _____

Write a different story event in each brick. Write the events in order.

① ② ③

④ ⑤ ⑥

Story Elements Chart

Name _____ Date _____

Book title: _____

Author: _____

- Characters:

- Problem:

- Setting:

- Solution:

- Main idea and supporting details:

The Ultimate Forms for All Reasons • ©The Mailbox® Books • TEC61337

READ THIS! Recommended by _____
student name

Title: _____

Author: _____

This book is about _____

_____

_____

_____

You should read it because _____

_____

The Ultimate Forms for All Reasons • ©The Mailbox® Books • TEC61337

- -

READ THIS! Recommended by _____
student name

Title: _____

Author: _____

This book is about _____

_____

_____

_____

You should read it because _____

_____

The Ultimate Forms for All Reasons • ©The Mailbox® Books • TEC61337

Would you like to be friends with the main character? Tell why or why not.

TEC61337

Describe the story's setting. Can you easily picture it? Why or why not?

TEC61337

What is the problem in the story? Tell how it is solved.

TEC61337

Talk about the most interesting thing that happens in the story.

TEC61337

The theme of a story is a message the author wants to share about life. What do you think the author of your book is trying to say?

TEC61337

If you could talk with the author, what questions would you ask?

TEC61337

Compare this book to the last one you read. How is it the same? How is it different?

TEC61337

Compare the main character with the main character in the last book you read. Would the two get along? Why or why not?

TEC61337

Is this story fiction or nonfiction? Tell how you know.

TEC61337

Tell about a part of the story that reminds you of something from your own life.

TEC61337

In what genre does your book belong? Tell why it fits in that genre.

TEC61337

If you could change one thing about your book, what would you change? Why?

TEC61337

The Ultimate Forms for All Reasons • ©The Mailbox® Books • TEC61337

Note to the teacher: After each student has completed an independent reading assignment, pair students and give each pair a copy of this page. Direct the pair to cut apart the cards. Then have students take turns drawing a card, reading it aloud, and then talking about her book in response to the topic. Or use the cards to have a discussion about a class read-aloud.

74

Book Report

Name _____

Title: _____

_____

Author: _____

Type of book: _____ Number of pages: _____

Summary of the book: _____

_____

_____

_____

_____

_____

Choose a character, an event, or an idea from the book that reminds you of something from your life.

_____

Explain your choice. _____

_____

_____

_____

_____

VOCABULARY BOOKMARK

Meaning

1. _____

Name _____

2. _____

Title & Author

3. _____

4. _____

Word   **Page**

5. _____

1. _____

6. _____

2. _____

3. _____

7. _____

4. _____

5. _____

8. _____

6. _____

7. _____

9. _____

8. _____

9. _____

10. _____

10. _____

Fold.

TEC61337

Note to the teacher: Give each student a copy of the bookmark. Before beginning reading, have the student cut out the bookmark, personalize it, and then fold it along the dashed line. Direct the student to use the bookmark to keep his page and to record ten new words and their meanings as he reads.

"Bee" a Super Speller!

Use the chart below to help you study your spelling words. Put a check mark after you complete each step.

Spelling Words	1 Say the word.	2 Say the letters.	3 Close your eyes and spell the word.	4 Check your spelling.	5 Cover the word. Write the word.	6 Check your spelling.

The Ultimate Forms for All Reasons • ©The Mailbox® Books • TEC61337

Note to the teacher: At the beginning of each week, make one or more copies of this guide for each student to use while studying her spelling words. Instruct her to draw a check mark in each of columns 1–4 as she completes them. Then, in column 5, have her write the word from memory.

Writing Rubric

Student's name: _____ Date: _____

Title of writing: _____

	Agree	Disagree
1. The writing selection has a topic sentence and concluding sentence.		
2. The purpose of the writing is clear (e.g. narrative, descriptive, explanatory, persuasive, etc.).		
3. The writing selection shows a logical order.		
4. The writing selection makes sense; it is easy to read.		
5. Specific details are used to enhance the explained steps.		
6. All details relate to the topic.		
7. Descriptive words and details are used.		
8. Transitional words—such as *first, next, then,* and *finally*—are used.		
9. Proper punctuation and capitalization are used.		
10. Each word is spelled correctly.		
11. Run-on sentences and incomplete sentences are avoided.		
12. Each verb agrees with its subject.		
13. All proper nouns are capitalized.		
14. Each paragraph is indented.		

Comments: _____

_____

_____

_____

_____

_____

The Ultimate Forms for All Reasons • ©The Mailbox® Books • TEC61337

ADDITION FACTS

TEC61337

SUBTRACTION FACTS

TEC61337

MULTIPLICATION FACTS

TEC61337

DIVISION FACTS

TEC61337

The Ultimate Forms for All Reasons • ©The Mailbox® Books • TEC61337

Note to the teacher: Program a copy of the operation you are currently studying. Then give one copy to each student to use for practice.

_____ 's

Science Journal

Name _____   Date _____

_____
science investigation

1 Briefly describe the investigation. _____
_____

2 What special materials, if any, were used? _____
_____

3 Write about what you learned. _____
_____

4 On the back of this sheet, draw and label a diagram or picture to describe the science investigation.

Note to the teacher: Give each student one copy of the journal cover and several journal pages. Have her staple the pages behind the cover. Instruct her to complete a page after a lab activity, an experiment, or another science activity.

Research Report Rubric

Name: _____ Date: _____ Topic: _____

	3 points	2 points	1 point	0 points
Content and Details	Content is very informative and accurate. Report has many supporting details and is interesting to read.	Content is informative and mostly accurate. Report has adequate details.	Content is not always related to the topic. Many inaccuracies. Few supporting details.	Content is not relevant or accurate. No details.
Organization	Report is well organized with a strong beginning, middle, and ending.	Report shows adequate organization. It has a beginning, a middle, and an ending.	Report is poorly organized and confusing at times.	Report has no organization.
Writing Mechanics and Readability	Report has few or no errors in spelling, punctuation, and/or grammar. Report is easy to read.	Report has a few errors in spelling, punctuation, and/or grammar. Report is readable.	Report has several errors in spelling, punctuation, and/or grammar. Report is difficult to read.	Report is unreadable.
Notecards	Notecards are completed and labeled correctly.	Most notecards are completed and labeled correctly.	Some notecards are completed and labeled correctly.	No notecards.
Bibliography	Bibliography is completed and written in correct form.	Bibliography is done but incomplete in parts. Some errors in form.	Bibliography is incomplete. Many errors in form.	No bibliography.
Other				

Total points: _____

The Ultimate Forms for All Reasons • ©The Mailbox® Books • TEC61337

Note to the teacher: Make one copy for each student. Use the rubric for grading purposes. Or have the student use it to evaluate her own work, lightly shading each box that describes her report.

Super Study Skills

COMPLETING ASSIGNMENTS

- Know exactly what your assignment is and when it is due.
- Decide how much time you'll need.
- Plan a time to do the assignment.
- Choose a quiet place to work.
- Gather all the books, paper, pencils, markers, and folders you'll need.
- Read the directions carefully.
- Decide how much of the assignment you'll finish before taking a break.
- Do the assignment neatly; then check it for mistakes.

MANAGING YOUR TIME

- Make a daily to-do list. Cross out each task as you complete it.
- Use a calendar to mark when different assignments are due. Plan your work and play time around these due dates.
- Work on your toughest assignments during the time of day when you work best.
- Make a hard assignment, such as a research project, easier by breaking it down into smaller parts. Decide how much of the assignment you'll need to finish by certain days in order to meet the due date.

TAKING NOTES

- Listen carefully.
- Write down only the important words and phrases.
- Use abbreviations and symbols whenever you can.
- Highlight the most important details.

TAKING TESTS

Essay Tests
- Read the question twice to make sure you understand whether you are to *compare/contrast, define, describe, explain, list,* or *prove* your answer.
- Change the test question into the first sentence of your answer.
- Decide on the best order for the details of your answer.
- Reread your answer to make sure nothing was left out.

True/False Tests
- Read the whole question before answering it.
- Look for words—such as *all, every, always,* and *never*—that often make a statement false.
- To mark an answer true, all parts of it must be true. If only part of a statement is true, mark it false.

Matching Tests
- Read both lists before making any matches.
- Unless the directions say you can use an answer more than once, cross out each answer as you match it.

Multiple-Choice Tests
- Read the directions to find out if you're to look for the *correct* answer or the *best* answer.
- Read *all* the answer choices before deciding on your answer.
- Look for tricky words—such as *not, never, except,* and *unless*—that can change a question's meaning.

Fill-in-the-Blank Tests
- Count the number of blanks in each question to know how many words to write for an answer.
- Decide what word or number best answers that question and write it in the blank.

The Ultimate Forms for All Reasons • ©The Mailbox® Books • TEC61337

82 **Note to the teacher:** Give a copy of this sheet to each student. Direct him to keep it in a work folder or notebook to use as a reference.

Name _____

Chapter Chart

This simple chart can help you remember important information that you read. As you read an assignment, write a question for each page in the space below. Record the page number where the answer can be found. Then write the answer. When you've finished reading the entire assignment, write a few sentences telling what you learned in the summary space. What an easy way to study!

Page Read	Question	Answer	Page Number of Answer

Summary:

The Ultimate Forms for All Reasons • ©The Mailbox® Books • TEC61337

Note to the teacher: Give a copy of this chart to each student whenever he reads in his textbook or other information source. Have him keep his completed charts in a folder to use when studying for a unit test.

Look What's Coming!

Dear Parent(s),

Your child has an important project due on _____.
due date

Please review the project details below with your child. Then help your child
organize his/her time wisely and plan ahead to meet the deadline. Have your child
return the signed portion of this form to school.

_____   _____
teacher signature   date

Project title _____

Materials needed _____

_____

Project information _____

_____

_____

_____

Additional comments _____

_____

The Ultimate Forms for All Reasons • ©The Mailbox® Books • TEC61337

I have read and understand the project information above. I will work with a parent

to develop a plan so that my project is completed by _____.
due date

Student signature: _____

Parent signature: _____

Note to the teacher: Complete a copy of this page with information for a project. Give each child a copy prior to the due date.

Center Checklist

Name _____ Date(s) _____

Center	Date Completed	Comments

The Ultimate Forms for All Reasons • ©The Mailbox® Books • TEC61337

Note to the teacher: Program the first column with your classroom centers; then make a class supply. Have each child write in the corresponding row after completing a center.

TEC61337

TEC61337

TEC61337

TEC61337

TEC61337

TEC61337

The Ultimate Forms for All Reasons • ©The Mailbox® Books • TEC61337

Note to the teacher: Program copies of the cards as desired. Consider using them for vocabulary words, study guides, math facts, center activities, or writing prompts. Color-code the borders if necessary.

Assessment

Skill Remediation Record

Remediation Tracker for _____
student

| Skill to Remediate | Date | Notes |

Student Anecdote

Anecdotal Records for _____
student

Subject:

Date: _____ Subject: _____

Observation notes:

Skills Assessment

Skills Assessment Checklist

Student _____

Teacher _____

Date _____

Subject _____

Skill/Objective	Mastery of Skill		
	Yes	No	N/A

Student Self-Evaluations

Student Self-Evaluation

Date: _____

Name: _____

Work sample: _____

I chose this work because _____

...t best describes your work.

Poor

Totals:

Good

Student Self-Evaluation

Name: _____ Date: _____

Work sample: _____

I chose this work because _____

_____

Draw a ✓ in the box that best describes your work.

	Good	Fair	Poor
1. I completed my work.			
2. I used my time wisely.			
3. I followed all directions.			
4. My work is free of errors.			
5. I am proud of my work.			

Totals:

Good _____

Fair _____

Poor _____

On the back of this sheet, explain what you would do differently.

Student Group-Work Evaluation

Name: _____ Date: _____

Group project: _____

Group members: _____

Draw a ✓ in the box that best describes your work.

	Good	Fair	Poor
1. I worked well with all group members.			
2. All group members helped equally.			
3. I followed all directions.			
4. I enjoyed working with this group.			

Totals:

Good _____

Fair _____

Poor _____

On the back of this sheet, write about what you learned.

Skills Assessment Checklist

Student _____   Date _____

Teacher _____   Subject _____

Mastery of Skill

Skill/Objective	Yes	No	N/A	Notes

Skills Progress Assessment

Date _____

Skills/Objectives

Key
- ✓ = mastery
- ✗ = no mastery
- • = unsure

1.														
2.														
3.														
4.														
5.														
6.														
7.														
8.														
9.														
10.														
11.														
12.														
13.														
14.														
15.														
16.														
17.														
18.														
19.														
20.														
21.														
22.														
23.														
24.														
25.														
26.														
27.														
28.														
29.														
30.														

Anecdotal Records for _____

student

Date: _____ Subject: _____

Observation notes:

Date: _____ Subject: _____

Observation notes:

Date: _____ Subject: _____

Observation notes:

Date: _____ Subject: _____

Observation notes:

Additional comments/follow-up: _____

_____

_____

_____

The Ultimate Forms for All Reasons • ©The Mailbox® Books • TEC61337

Note to the teacher: Write observations directly on the form or attach a full-size sticky note to each box for extra writing space.

Remediation Tracker for _____
student

Skill to Remediate	Date	Notes

Communication

Progress Report

Name _____ Date _____

Teacher _____

- Literacy
- Math
- Science/Social Studies

Behavior
- [ ] Excelle... ...ing Improvem...
- [ ] Good ...men...

Classroom News

Class Newsletter: Back-to-School

Date: _____

Teacher: _____

Parent-Teacher Conference Report

Date: _____
Student: _____
Teacher: _____

Work Habits

	Excellent	Satisfactory	Needs Improvement	Unsatisfactory
Listens while others talk				
Follows directions				
Works independently				
Works accurately				
Works neatly				
Completes work on time				

Attitudes

Gets alon...
Is ...
D...
Sh...
Care...
Assu...

Comme...

Subjec...

Conference Questionnaire

Parent Conference Questionnaire

Dear _____,

...please take a few minutes to answer the questions below. Your ... ...e prepare for our upcoming conference. I look forward ...

You're Invited!

Please come to an open house for

_____
teacher

Date: _____

Time: _____ Room: _____

Hope to see you there!

The Ultimate Forms for All Reasons • ©The Mailbox® Books • TEC61337

You're Invited!

Please come to an open house for

_____
teacher

Date: _____

Time: _____ Room: _____

Hope to see you there!

The Ultimate Forms for All Reasons • ©The Mailbox® Books • TEC61337

You're Invited!

Please come to an open house for

_____
teacher

Date: _____

Time: _____ Room: _____

Hope to see you there!

The Ultimate Forms for All Reasons • ©The Mailbox® Books • TEC61337

You're Invited!

Please come to an open house for

_____
teacher

Date: _____

Time: _____ Room: _____

Hope to see you there!

The Ultimate Forms for All Reasons • ©The Mailbox® Books • TEC61337

Welcome to Open House!

Teacher: _____   Date: _____

Please sign in.

Your Name	Child's Name
1.	
2.	
3.	
4.	
5.	
6.	
7.	
8.	
9.	
10.	
11.	
12.	
13.	
14.	
15.	
16.	
17.	
18.	
19.	
20.	
21.	
22.	
23.	
24.	
25.	
26.	
27.	
28.	
29.	
30.	

Thank you for attending our open house. We appreciate your support!

Sincerely,

_____
teacher

Thank you for attending our open house. We appreciate your support!

Sincerely,

_____
teacher

Thank you for attending our open house. We appreciate your support!

Sincerely,

_____
teacher

Thank you for attending our open house. We appreciate your support!

Sincerely,

_____
teacher

Dear Parent,

Your conference for _____ has been scheduled at _____ on _____. Please complete the bottom portion of this form and return it to me by _____.

date

I'm looking forward to visiting with you.

Sincerely,

_____
teacher

☐ I plan to attend my child's conference at the scheduled time.

☐ I will need to reschedule our conference. Please call me at _____ to reschedule.
phone number

_____   _____
child's name   parent signature

The Ultimate Forms for All Reasons • ©The Mailbox® Books • TEC61337

Dear Parent,

Your conference for _____ has been scheduled at _____ on _____. Please complete the bottom portion of this form and return it to me by _____.

date

I'm looking forward to visiting with you.

Sincerely,

_____
teacher

☐ I plan to attend my child's conference at the scheduled time.

☐ I will need to reschedule our conference. Please call me at _____ to reschedule.
phone number

_____   _____
child's name   parent signature

The Ultimate Forms for All Reasons • ©The Mailbox® Books • TEC61337

Conference Questionnaire

Dear _____,

    Please take a few minutes to answer the questions below. Your responses will help me prepare for our upcoming conference. I look forward to meeting with you on _____.

    Please return this questionnaire before our scheduled conference day.

Thank you,

_____
teacher

What subject(s) does your child enjoy most? _____

Why? _____

_____

_____

What subject(s) seems difficult for your child? _____

Why? _____

_____

_____

Describe your child's attitude toward school. _____

_____

_____

Does your child participate in any after-school activities? _____

If so, please list them: _____

_____

Please list any concerns that you would like to address during our conference.

_____

_____

_____

The Ultimate Forms for All Reasons • ©The Mailbox® Books • TEC61337

Parent-Teacher Conference Report

Date: _____

Student: _____

Teacher: _____

Work Habits

	Excellent	Satisfactory	Needs Improvement	Unsatisfactory
Listens while others talk				
Follows directions				
Works independently				
Works accurately				
Works neatly				
Completes work on time				

Attitudes

	Excellent	Satisfactory	Needs Improvement	Unsatisfactory
Gets along with others				
Is courteous and cooperates				
Demonstrates self-control				
Shows respect for others				
Cares for personal property				
Assumes responsibility for actions				

Subjects

	Progress				Effort			
	Excellent	Satisfactory	Needs Improvement	Unsatisfactory	Excellent	Satisfactory	Needs Improvement	Unsatisfactory
Reading								
Math								
Handwriting								
Spelling								
Science								
Social Studies								
Language								
Other:								

Special Subjects

	Excellent	Satisfactory	Needs Improvement	Unsatisfactory	Excellent	Satisfactory	Needs Improvement	Unsatisfactory
Art								
Music								
Media Center								
Computer								
P.E.								
Other:								

Comments: _____

_____

_____

Teacher signature: _____

Parent signature: _____

The Ultimate Forms for All Reasons • ©The Mailbox® Books • TEC61337

Conference Schedule for _____ on _____

teacher   date

AM

7:00	_____
7:15	_____
7:30	_____
7:45	_____
8:00	_____
8:15	_____
8:30	_____
8:45	_____
9:00	_____
9:15	_____
9:30	_____
9:45	_____
10:00	_____
10:15	_____
10:30	_____
10:45	_____
11:00	_____
11:15	_____
11:30	_____
11:45	_____

PM

12:00	_____
12:15	_____
12:30	_____
12:45	_____
1:00	_____

PM

1:15	_____
1:30	_____
1:45	_____
2:00	_____
2:15	_____
2:30	_____
2:45	_____
3:00	_____
3:15	_____
3:30	_____
3:45	_____
4:00	_____
4:15	_____
4:30	_____
4:45	_____
5:00	_____
5:15	_____
5:30	_____
5:45	_____
6:00	_____
6:15	_____
6:30	_____
6:45	_____
7:00	_____
7:15	_____
7:30	_____
7:45	_____

The Ultimate Forms for All Reasons • ©The Mailbox® Books • TEC61337

Thank you for coming to your child's parent-teacher conference. Your attendance is appreciated!

Sincerely,

_____
teacher

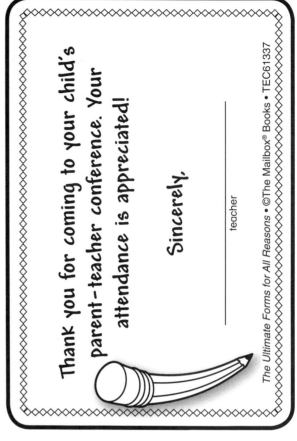

The Ultimate Forms for All Reasons • ©The Mailbox® Books • TEC61337

Thank you for coming to your child's parent-teacher conference. Your attendance is appreciated!

Sincerely,

_____
teacher

The Ultimate Forms for All Reasons • ©The Mailbox® Books • TEC61337

Thank you for coming to your child's parent-teacher conference. Your attendance is appreciated!

Sincerely,

_____
teacher

The Ultimate Forms for All Reasons • ©The Mailbox® Books • TEC61337

Thank you for coming to your child's parent-teacher conference. Your attendance is appreciated!

Sincerely,

_____
teacher

The Ultimate Forms for All Reasons • ©The Mailbox® Books • TEC61337

Classroom News

Teacher: _____ Date: _____

The Ultimate Forms for All Reasons • ©The Mailbox® Books • TEC61337

Classroom News

Teacher: _____   Date: _____

Classroom News

Teacher: _____   Date: _____

The Ultimate Forms for All Reasons • ©The Mailbox® Books • TEC61337

Classroom News

Teacher: _____   Date: _____

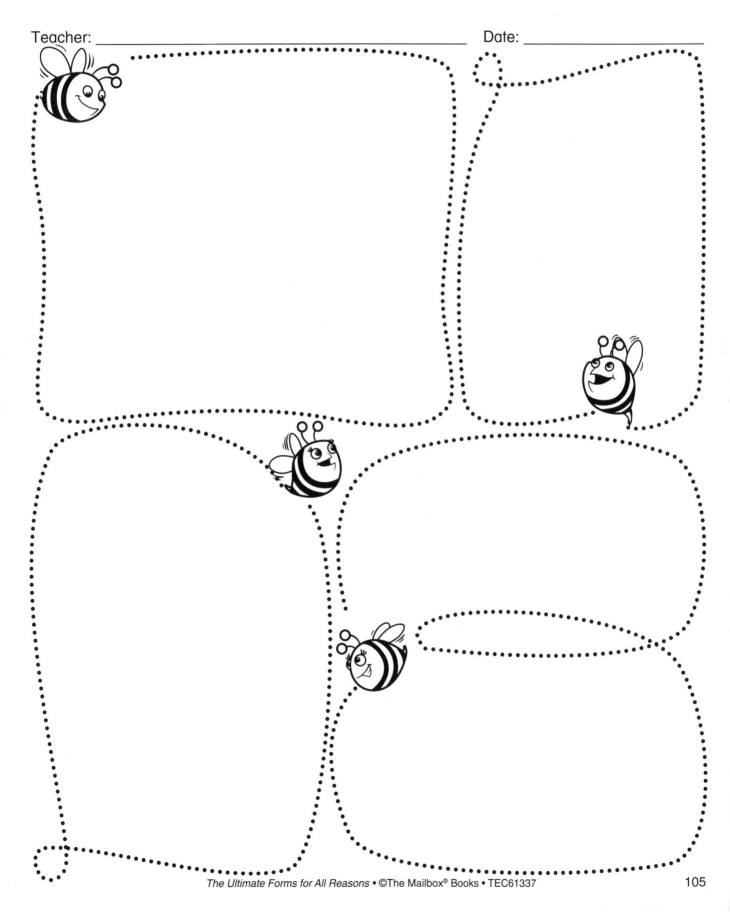

Classroom News

Teacher: _____ Date: _____

The Ultimate Forms for All Reasons • ©The Mailbox® Books • TEC61337

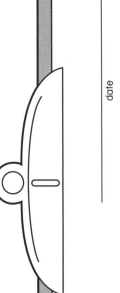

Missed Assignments

_____
date

Dear Parent,

_____ needs to complete
the following assignments:

_____

_____

_____

_____

_____

The work is due by _____.

Sincerely,

_____
teacher

_____
parent

Please sign and return.

The Ultimate Forms for All Reasons • ©The Mailbox® Books • TEC61337

Missed Assignments

_____
date

Dear Parent,

_____ needs to complete
the following assignments:

_____

_____

_____

_____

_____

The work is due by _____.

Sincerely,

_____
teacher

_____
parent

Please sign and return.

The Ultimate Forms for All Reasons • ©The Mailbox® Books • TEC61337

Your Help at Home Is Needed.

_____
date

Dear Parent,

_____ needs extra help with
student

_____ .

Please use the idea(s) below to help your child at home.

_____

_____

_____

_____

_____

_____
teacher

Thank you!

The Ultimate Forms for All Reasons • ©The Mailbox® Books • TEC61337

Your Help at Home Is Needed.

_____
date

Dear Parent,

_____ needs extra help with
student

_____ .

Please use the idea(s) below to help your child at home.

_____

_____

_____

_____

_____

_____
teacher

Thank you!

The Ultimate Forms for All Reasons • ©The Mailbox® Books • TEC61337

Progress Report • • • • • • • • • • • Date _____

Name _____ Teacher _____

Literacy

Math

Science/Social Studies

Tests/Quizzes

Comments: _____
_____
_____
_____

Behavior
☐ Excellent ☐ Showing Improvement
☐ Good ☐ Needs Improvement

PLEASE SIGN AND RETURN.

_____
parent

The Ultimate Forms for All Reasons • ©The Mailbox® Books • TEC61337

Weekly Progress Report

Name _____

Week _____

Work Habits
☐ Works independently and completes work
☐ Needs some assistance
☐ Needs a great deal of assistance
☐ Is easily distracted

Effort/Attitude
☐ Excellent
☐ Good
☐ Average
☐ Needs improvement

Behavior
☐ Excellent
☐ Good
☐ Showing improvement
☐ Needs improvement

Comments:

_____ teacher

_____ parent

PLEASE SIGN AND RETURN.

The Ultimate Forms for All Reasons • ©The Mailbox® Books • TEC61337

This Week's Papers

Attached is your child's work from this week as well as any other important notes. After reviewing the papers, please sign and return this sheet.

Thank you!

Date

_____
parent signature

Comments:

This Week's Papers

Attached is your child's work from this week as well as any other important notes. After reviewing the papers, please sign and return this sheet.

Thank you!

Date

_____
parent signature

Comments:

REMINDER!

Library books
are due

_____.
date

The Ultimate Forms for All Reasons • ©The Mailbox® Books • TEC61337

REMINDER!

Library books
are due

_____.
date

The Ultimate Forms for All Reasons • ©The Mailbox® Books • TEC61337

REMINDER!

Library books
are due

_____.
date

The Ultimate Forms for All Reasons • ©The Mailbox® Books • TEC61337

REMINDER!

Library books
are due

_____.
date

The Ultimate Forms for All Reasons • ©The Mailbox® Books • TEC61337

School Supplies Needed

Your child needs the following school supplies. Please send them in by _____.
date

☐ _____   ☐ _____

☐ _____   ☐ _____

☐ _____   ☐ _____

☐ _____   ☐ _____

☐ _____   ☐ _____

Thank you!

The Ultimate Forms for All Reasons • ©The Mailbox® Books • TEC61337

_____'s Classroom Wish List
teacher

If you are able to donate any of the checked items, our class will appreciate your kindness.

☐ antibacterial wipes   ☐ _____

☐ hand sanitizer   ☐ _____

☐ resealable plastic bags   ☐ _____

☐ tissues   ☐ _____

☐ markers   Thank you!   ☐ _____

☐ glue sticks   ☐ _____

☐ glue bottles   ☐ _____

The Ultimate Forms for All Reasons • ©The Mailbox® Books • TEC61337

Dear Parent,

Our class is preparing for a special class project. If possible, please send to school any of the items listed below by _____.
date

★ _____   ★ _____

★ _____   ★ _____

★ _____   ★ _____

★ _____   **Thank you!**

_____
teacher

Dear Parent,

Our class is celebrating _____

on _____. We will need families to
date

send in snacks and supplies. If you could send _____

_____ to

school, we would greatly appreciate it. If you are unable to send

in the item(s) requested, please let me know.

Thank you!   Sincerely,

_____
teacher

Going on a Field Trip

Dear Parent,

We are planning a trip to _____

_____

on _____. We will leave at _____ and return
       date

by _____. Your child will need to bring

⬡ _____

⬡ _____

⬡ _____

Please return the signed permission slip to school by _____.
       date

Sincerely,

_____
teacher

The Ultimate Forms for All Reasons • ©The Mailbox® Books • TEC61337

_____ has my permission to go on the field trip
child's name

to _____ on _____.
   location   date

_____   _____
parent signature   date

114

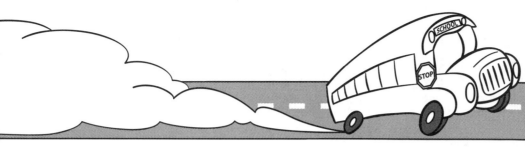

_____ 's Field Trip Group
chaperone

Students in Your Group

Teacher: _____

Emergency Phone #: _____

School Phone #: _____

Other Important Information

A Field Trip Recap

Name _____ Date _____

Location _____

I enjoyed _____

_____

_____

I learned _____

_____

_____

_____

Color to rate the trip.

    5 stars = I had an awesome time!

    1 star = I didn't enjoy the trip.

Explain. _____

_____

_____

_____

The Ultimate Forms for All Reasons • ©The Mailbox® Books • TEC61337

Money Due

Dear Parent,

_____ owes _____
student   amount

for _____ .
reason

Please return the money to school in an envelope by

_____ .
date

Sincerely,

_____
teacher

The Ultimate Forms for All Reasons • ©The Mailbox® Books • TEC61337

Money Due

Dear Parent,

_____ owes _____
student   amount

for _____ .
reason

Please return the money to school in an envelope by

_____ .
date

Sincerely,

_____
teacher

The Ultimate Forms for All Reasons • ©The Mailbox® Books • TEC61337

Money Due

Dear Parent,

_____ owes _____
student   amount

for _____ .
reason

Please return the money to school in an envelope by

_____ .
date

Sincerely,

_____
teacher

The Ultimate Forms for All Reasons • ©The Mailbox® Books • TEC61337

Injury Report

_____
date

Dear Parent,

This is to report that _____ was injured at school.
name

Injury: _____

Treatment: _____

Treated by: _____

Follow-up suggestions: _____

_____

Please sign and return this notice.   Thank you.

_____
teacher signature

_____   _____
parent signature   date

The Ultimate Forms for All Reasons • ©The Mailbox® Books • TEC61337

Injury Report

_____
date

Dear Parent,

This is to report that _____ was injured at school.
name

Injury: _____

Treatment: _____

Treated by: _____

Follow-up suggestions: _____

_____

Please sign and return this notice.   Thank you.

_____
teacher signature

_____   _____
parent signature   date

The Ultimate Forms for All Reasons • ©The Mailbox® Books • TEC61337

INCIDENT REPORT

Student: _____ Report by: _____

Date: _____ Time of incident: _____

Staff member who witnessed incident: _____
signature

What happened?

_____

_____

_____

_____

Follow up:

_____

_____

_____

_____

PARENT CONTACT INFORMATION

Parent contacted: yes   no   Time: _____

Notes about conversation: _____

_____

_____

Please sign and return   _____
parent

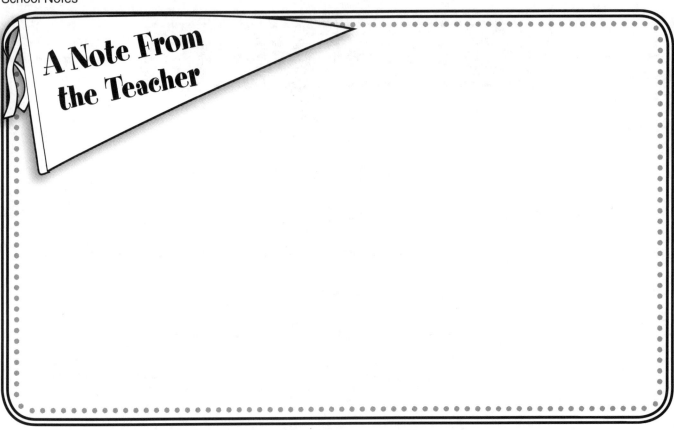

The Ultimate Forms for All Reasons • ©The Mailbox® Books • TEC61337

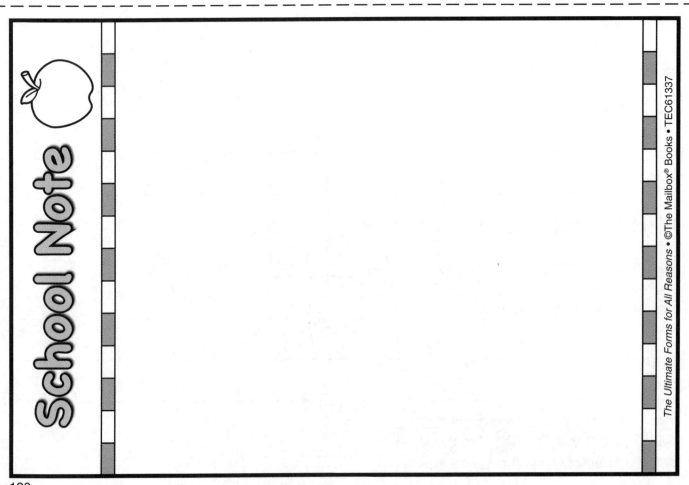

We're Celebrating!

Dear Parent,

We are celebrating _____

_____

at _____ on _____,
        time   day

_____. Please help us
                     date

celebrate by _____

_____

_____

_____.

Thank you!

     Sincerely,

     _____
                      teacher

The Ultimate Forms for All Reasons • ©The Mailbox® Books • TEC61337

You're Invited!

We are celebrating _____

_____.

When: _____
                           date/time

Where: _____

We hope you can join us!

The Ultimate Forms for All Reasons • ©The Mailbox® Books • TEC61337

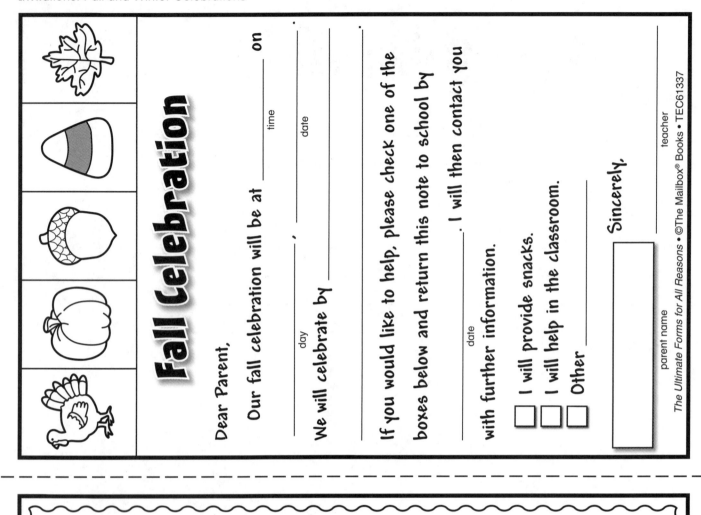

Fall Celebration

Dear Parent,

Our fall celebration will be at _____ on _____ .
time

_____ , _____ .
day   date

We will celebrate by _____

If you would like to help, please check one of the boxes below and return this note to school by _____ . I will then contact you
date

with further information.

☐ I will provide snacks.
☐ I will help in the classroom.
☐ Other _____

Sincerely,

_____
parent name

_____
teacher

The Ultimate Forms for All Reasons • ©The Mailbox® Books • TEC61337

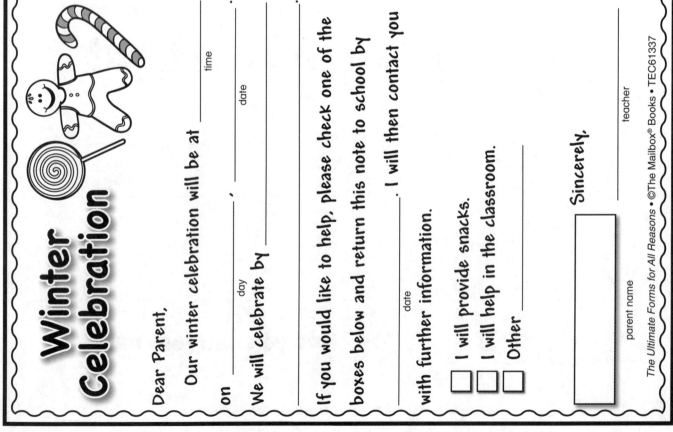

Winter Celebration

Dear Parent,

Our winter celebration will be at _____ .
time

on _____ , _____ .
day   date

We will celebrate by _____

If you would like to help, please check one of the boxes below and return this note to school by _____ . I will then contact you
date

with further information.

☐ I will provide snacks.
☐ I will help in the classroom.
☐ Other _____

Sincerely,

_____
parent name

_____
teacher

The Ultimate Forms for All Reasons • ©The Mailbox® Books • TEC61337

Valentine's Day Celebration

Dear Parent,

Our Valentine's Day celebration will be at _____ on _____, _____.
time   day

We will celebrate by _____.
                     date

If you would like to help, please check one of the boxes below and return this note to school by _____. I will then contact you with further information.
                   date

☐ I will provide snacks.
☐ I will help in the classroom.
☐ Other _____

Sincerely,

_____
parent name

_____
teacher

End-of-School Celebration

Dear Parent,

Our end-of-school celebration will be at _____ on _____, _____.
time   day

We will celebrate by _____.
                     date

If you would like to help, please check one of the boxes below and return this note to school by _____. I will then contact you with further information.
                   date

☐ I will provide snacks.
☐ I will help in the classroom.
☐ Other _____

Sincerely,

_____
parent name

_____
teacher

Valentine's Day Class List

Our Valentine's Day Class List

Teachers: _____

_____

Boys

Girls

_____ _____
_____ _____
_____ _____
_____ _____
_____ _____
_____ _____
_____ _____
_____ _____
_____ _____
_____ _____
_____ _____
_____ _____
_____ _____

Special instructions: _____

_____

Your help keeps me afloat.

_____
teacher

TEC61337

Thank you!

THANK you!

I simply can't thank you enough!

_____
teacher

Thank you!   Thank YOU!

Thank you!   Thank YOU!

Thank you!   THANK you!

TEC61337

From me to you,

a **HUGE**

thank you!

_____
teacher

TEC61337

Thanks a bunch!

TEC61337

The Ultimate Forms for All Reasons • ©The Mailbox® Books • TEC61337

Congratulations,

_____
name

You earned all-star status!

_____

_____

_____

_____
teacher

The Ultimate Forms for All Reasons • ©The Mailbox® Books • TEC61337

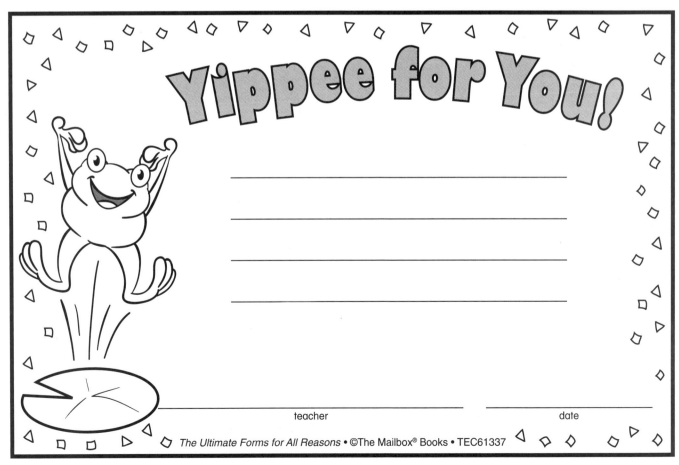

Yippee for You!

_____

_____

_____

_____

_____   _____
teacher   date

The Ultimate Forms for All Reasons • ©The Mailbox® Books • TEC61337

The Ultimate Forms for All Reasons • ©The Mailbox® Books • TEC61337

The Ultimate Forms for All Reasons • ©The Mailbox® Books • TEC61337